D1708770

the wandering wise men

By Eric and Meredith Schrotenboer

Illustrations by Joel Schoon-Tanis

To Meryn and Judah, may you always seek the one true Light, Jesus.

- Mom and Dad

To my Family (in all of its iterations) and the traditions we share.

- Joel

© 2021 Eric & Meredith Schrotenboer

All rights reserved. No part of this publication may be reproduced, stored in a retrieval system, or transmitted in any form or by any means electronic, mechanical, photocopying, recording or otherwise, without the prior written permission of the publisher.

Published by
Fresh Wind Studios | Grand Rapids, MI

Publisher's Cataloging-in-Publication Data
Schrotenboer, Eric.

The wandering wise men / by Eric Schrotenboer & Meredith Schrotenboer ; illustrator, Joel Schoon-Tanis. – Grand Rapids, MI : Fresh Wind Studios, 2021.

p. ; cm.

ISBN13: 978-0-9601089-0-9

1. Jesus Christ--Juvenile literature. 2. Magi--Juvenile literature. 3. Bible stories, English--Juvenile literature. I. Title. II. Schrotenboer, Meredith. III. Tanis, Joel E.

BS551.3.S44 2021
220.9505--dc23

Printed in the P.R.C. by Artron Art Printing (HK) Limited,
Print and logistics management by M.J. Jacobs LLC (ArtBookPrinting.com) Grand Rapids, MI

First Printing, 2021

25 24 23 22 21 • 5 4 3 2 1

The illustrations for this book were done in acrylic paint on 300 lb. hot pressed Arches watercolor paper.

This book was edited by Crystal Bowman and designed by Mariah Scott and Aubree Berg.

Art direction by Eric Schrotenboer.

The Wandering Wise Men Tradition

The wise men wander through the night,
to find the Light that shines so bright.
So, look and find the wise men, three.
You never know where they might be.

In an ancient eastern city, before the morning light...

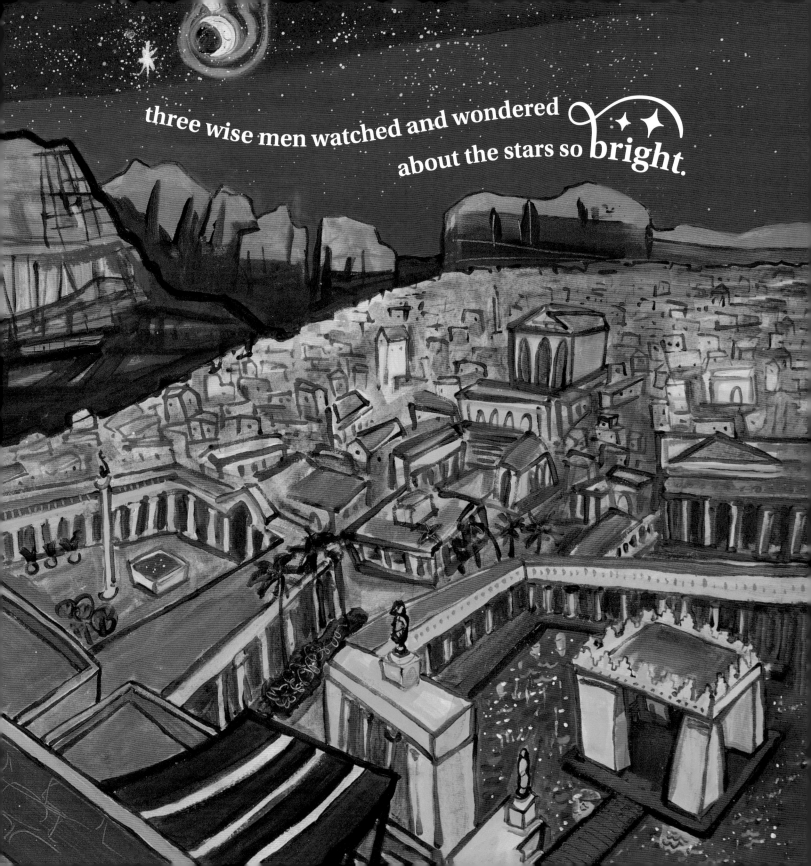

three wise men watched and wondered about the stars so bright.

They remembered Daniel the prophet
who spoke of signs in the sky,

marking the birth of a coming King —

a Savior from on high.

That very night the wise men saw a light that shone so **bright,** they knew the planets, stars, and moon had formed this **wondrous** sight.

"These are the signs we've waited for," they said with joyful grins.

"We need to find this newborn king, our adventure now begins."

God chose those curious wise men
from a far and distant land
by sending them a message
God knew they'd understand.

They packed their camels with treasures,
for it was time to go.

A King had been born in Judea;
soon all the world would know.

From out of the east they **traveled**
on roads that they knew well.
They **wandered** with fellow travelers
who carried goods to sell.

Across the desert they
journeyed
through sand and
blazing heat.

They only stopped to get a drink
and rest their tired feet.

The wise men came to Judea, where all roads finally led.

"Let's go up to Jerusalem,"
the weary wise men said.

King Herod the Great
was famous for his buildings,
tall and grand.

But many people feared this king
who ruled over all the land.

Up to Herod's palace they went
with caravan in tow...

to find out straight from Herod
all that he might know.

"Where's the child who has been born,
this brand-new Jewish king?
We saw his star up in the sky
and we have gifts to bring."

When Herod heard all their questions
he was worried and upset.
"I am the king of Judea,
and no one should forget!"

He called the chief priests together
and teachers of the law.

They opened up the *Word of God*
and told him what they saw.

"A ruler will **rise** from Bethlehem,"
the priests and teachers warned.

"He'll shepherd
God's people Israel,

this child who's
been born."

Herod called the three wise men
in hopes they would agree.

"Find this child in Bethlehem,
and then report to me."

"I want to worship the child too,
and bring a gift of my own."

But Herod was planning all along
to save his royal throne.

The **starry light** shone bright again
and led them on their way.

Over the town of Bethlehem the star appeared to stay.

"His name is Jesus," Mary said.

"The Lord has guided you."

In this moment, their eyes were opened
and they could finally see,

God had come
from heaven to earth
to be born like you and me.

The wise men bowed down to worship,
the Christ-child they adored.

They laid their gold and frankincense
and myrrh before the Lord.

An angel warned them in a dream
to go home a different way.

They knew they'd never be the same;
their lives were changed that day.

When the wise men left the child,
they knew they'd wander no more,

for they had found
in Bethlehem

what their hearts
were longing for.

The Light
still shines in the darkness,
for all the world to see.

Jesus reigns
as King today.

He shines through
you and me.